Potty Poets

SHARK

IN THE

TOILET!

SHARK

IN THE

TOILET!

WRITTEN AND ILLUSTRATED BY

CHRIS WHITE

The King's England Press

2004

ISBN 1 872438 96 2

Shark in the Toilet! is typeset by Moose Manuscripts
in CAC Moose 15pt and published by

The King's England Press Ltd
Cambertown House, Commercial Road, Goldthorpe
Rotherham, South Yorkshire, S63 9BL

Printed and bound in Great Britain by

Antony Rowe Ltd.
Chippenham
Wiltshire

FOREWORD

If you were to describe **Chris White** you might say he's the boy-next-door type of a guy, a pretty regular bloke. But, on closer inspection, you'll find that there's nothing ordinary or average about this man at all and beneath the surface beats a heart of pure pottyness. Get Chris talking and you'll soon be discussing the existence of vegetarian vampires, the practical uses for pet armadillos and listening to tales of hamsters with one eye, ever-growing, ever-eating guinea pigs and tiny trolls who, once you've drifted off to sleep, fill your navel with fluff every night!

Chris encourages us to change our diet of game shows, pop wannabees and makeovers by pressing the off switch on the remote and picking up a book; this one in particular will provide far more healthy entertainment than staring at an electronic box. It's a rereshing change for someone to be putting the *image* back into *imagination*. Who needs reality T.V. when you can create your own, far more interesting, world with a bit of time and thought power.

Although Chris's scribblings are intended to be humorous it's not all fun and fantasy. Much of his verse manages to entertain while also making serious comments on people and life. So, when you're reading this book, remember to delve a bit deeper than the face value of the poems and you'll discover that, along with performance poet and cartoon illustrator, **Chris White** could also be described as a modern-day **Aesop**.

The Editor

5

'TO MY GIRL IN THE RIVER...'

SHARK IN THE TOILET!

SHARK IN THE TOILET! SHARK IN THE TOILET!
Please listen to what's on my mind!
It's not good for your health when you relieve yourself
And a shark bites you on your behind!

I don't know how long he's been there
I just know that I let out a shriek
When I sat down to go to the toilet
And he nibbled me on my left cheek!

SHARK IN THE TOILET! SHARK IN THE TOILET!
It's shocked me to my very soul!
I couldn't believe how his big jaws smiled back
As I peered into the bowl.

Now I don't want to startle you too much,
But things are looking quite grim.
He just sort of chuckled at me
As I threw rolls of Andrex at him!

SHARK IN THE TOILET! SHARK IN THE TOILET!
I'm beginning to think we can't win!
I just whacked him with the bog brush
But he sliced it in half with his fin!

I can't think of how to get rid of him;
I've run out of toilet rolls and brushes.
He just sort of bobs back to the surface
Even after two or three flushes!

SHARK IN THE TOILET! SHARK IN THE TOILET!
Won't someone please listen to me!
We have to get rid of him right now:
I really have to pee!

NEVER PUT PARENTS UP YOUR NOSE

Never put parents up your nose,
Clever it is not.
You'll just end up with a sticky Mum
And a Dad covered in snot.

THE GREAT STUPEEDO

I have to tell you all about
The worst magician I've ever seen.
He could saw a woman in two
But the mess left behind was obscene!

There were no white rabbits in his hat,
Just a piece of fluff.
And the only thing he could make disappear
Was his audience in a huff!

MY RABBIT

My rabbit likes to wear make-up,
I think it is a pity
How the other rabbits make fun of him
'Cos I think he looks quite pretty!

He's so fashion conscious
There's a mirror in his hutch!
Now he wants to get his ears pierced
But I think that'll cost way too much!

THE DAY
IT SOUNDED DIFFERENT

I knew that day when I woke up
Something wasn't right.
I think it was when my dog meowed
As I switched on the light.

"What's happening?" I thought as I ran downstairs
(After brushing my teeth of course!)
I sat down for breakfast, said "Morning!" to Mum
And she neighed at me like a big horse.

The bees in the garden were honking like geese!
The birds in the trees made me jump!
They were mooing like cows as I poured out my milk
And my cereal went Snap! Crackle! Trump!

I quickly got dressed and headed for school
But as I scurried down the street
All the people jabbered like monkeys
And the car horns were going Tweet! Tweet!

I met my best friend in the classroom and said,
"Something's happening, and I think it's big!"
My best friend stared at me, opened his mouth,
Then grunted just like a huge pig!

We sat in our seats - the teacher came in,
A cat outside started squeaking!
The class hamster lay clucking in his cage
As my teacher started speaking.

Then, even after all the strange sounds I'd heard,
This one made me more worried and tense.
I couldn't believe it! Imagine my surprise
As my teacher talked some sense!

FISHIN' FOR AN ANSWER

Now, something that's been bugging me,
And I'd like to share with you,
Is a question I've got about fishermen
And something that they do.

Please tell me, when they catch a fish
(And sometimes it takes all day)
Why do they throw it back again
So it can swim away?

Does the fisherman just want to delay him?
Does he want to make the fish late?
What if the fish had a hair appointment?
Or perhaps a red-hot date?

Just think - he might have a train to catch
Or a test booked for his eyes.
Fishermen, please leave the fish alone
So they can get on with their busy lives!

RIGOR MORTIS IN MY TORTOISE

My tortoise has rigor mortis.
I know they don't move a lot
But mine now doesn't move at all:
Rigor mortis he has got.

I thought he was very slow before
But now he won't walk, drink or eat.
Yep! My tortoise has rigor mortis -
I wonder if I kept the receipt?

BLEATY KA-BOOM, THE SHEEP OF DOOM

What's that sound? Can you hear it?
BAAA! KA-BOOM! BAAA! KA-BOOM!
It's what you will hear when Bleaty is near,
They call him The Sheep of Doom.

His Mum tried to raise him as best she could
But for her it was a shock
When this little sheep she could not keep
With the others in her flock.

Bleaty was a bit different, you see,
He had a mischievous streak.
He would completely shear his whole family
While they were all asleep!

16

Bleaty's Mum didn't know what to do
And she reached the end of her tether,
When, for goodness sake, he put glue in the lake
So the ducks' feathers stuck together!

Each farm animal signed a petition
And banished Bleaty to the old barn
Where he sat all alone, in the dark, on his own,
And plotted revenge on the farm.

For weeks and months he stayed in there
And it became one happy farm.
The animals smiled with no sheep running wild
To ruin their peace and their calm.

Meanwhile, in the darkness, a voice sneered:
"They're going to get such a surprise!
Soon Bleaty Ka-Boom, The Sheep of Doom,
Will pull the wool over their eyes!"

Quietly, in the dead of night,
Bleaty darted round the cow pasture
Sprinting this way and that, collecting cow pats,
So he could cause disaster!

He made a giant cow pat pile;
The smell was just appalling!
Then he blew them sky high, through the air they did fly!
On the animals they soon would be falling!

A SPLAT! here. A SPLOOSH! there
But they weren't landing in the right place!
It had all gone wrong and it wasn't too long
Before Bleaty got one in the face!

"Plan B!" Bleaty bleated, wiping poo from his brow
And holding a stick of dynamite.
To the chicken shed he ran, "Let's see if I can
Give these dumb chickens a fright!"

As he slid the dynamite under a chicken
He cackled at what was to come.
"What better revenge than to blow up some hens
By sticking explosives up their bum!"

But the clever chicken noticed (just in time!)
The dynamite in between her legs.
The hens they scattered while Bleaty got splattered
By a shower of freshly-laid eggs!

Dripping with cow pats and hens' eggs
Bleaty yelled, "Plan C's the deciding factor!
Let's see the reaction when I leap into action
And attack the farmer's new tractor!"

The Sheep of Doom grabbed a potato
And shoved it up the exhaust!
"When the farmer turns the key," he cackled with glee,
"It will cause much mayhem of course!"

But when the tractor was started
No explosions, it just jolted the brake.
The tractor shot down the track, hit Bleaty
with a **WHACK!** catapulting him into the lake!

"This wasn't the plan!" Bleaty baaa-ed at the moon,
"It just isn't working!" he sighed.
"I've ended up soaked, covered with yolk
And smelling like a cow's backside!"

"Perhaps you need someone to talk to!"
Said an old cow leaning over the fence.
"If you get it all out, this anger and doubt,
It might make you feel less tense."

So they talked and talked for hours,
Until the sun came up the next day.
Bleaty knew he'd been wrong, that we should all get along
And destroying things isn't the way.

"The chickens live their lives, the pigs do their thing,
Each animal has different needs.
I shouldn't cause them harm, we all live on the farm,
Even though we are all different breeds."

"Some may have brown fur, some red feathers,
A few of us have a white fleece.
Let's not take, but give! Live and let live!"
So says Bleaty Ka-Boom, Sheep of Peace.

So from that day on Bleaty changed his ways;
The black sheep of the family learned his lesson.
He's much happier now thanks to his friend the cow
And a really good cow-ncelling session!

And that's the tale of Bleaty the sheep
Who's now stopped his raves and his rants.
Perfect he ain't and I'm not saying he's a saint,
All I'm saying is give sheep a chance.

23

NEVER PUT PETS UP YOUR NOSE

Never put pets up your nose,
It's dangerous and naughty.
Though you think you will not see them again
They'll fall back down when you're forty.

KEITH

Do you see over there
On that big, green leaf?
It's a butterfly:
His name is Keith.

But he's not a real butterfly,
If you know what I mean,
As he doesn't like butter -
He prefers margarine.

FRANKENHAMSTER

He died one tragic winter's night;
I didn't have a clue
That my hamster's final resting place
Would be under my Auntie's shoe.

They said he'd never live again,
That my experiments were frightening.
But they reckoned without my toaster
And a well-placed bolt of lightning.

I placed my hamster in the slot for bread,
The lightning struck the appliance
And he popped out lightly toasted but alive;
It's a wonder of modern science!

Sure, he looks a little odd.
He's whiffy, but what the heck!
He's my very own Frankenhamster
With a bolt through his furry neck.

He walks around like he did before,
Though sometimes he's splutterin' and coughin'.
You wouldn't really know he's dead
Except sometimes bits drop off him.

But I'll never need to feed him again!
So I think, you will discover,
As long as I charge him up overnight
It's cheaper than buying another!

UG!

Pull up stone and listen.
My name is UG! - ok?
They call me UG! coz only word
My Mum and Dad could say.

UG! thought he write a poem.
It take a while I bet.
I'm writing with a chisel –
There are no biros yet.

My only clothes are leopard fur;
Nothing ever fits.
I wish someone make Y-fronts
To warm my chilly bits.

This morning invented wheel,
Afternoon invented car
But tomorrow inventing traffic jam
So not get very far.

It boring being caveman,
Not much to do at all.
Until someone invent T.V.
Me just draw on the wall.

Me rent a little cave for one,
One day I like to buy.
But must meet Mrs UG! first
As mortgages sky high!

But women say UG! hairy
And they not like it when I belch!
But they all ugly anyway
Except that Raquel Welch.

UG! had pet pterodactyl
With huge wings and big beak.
Me had to have him put down though –
He ate Grandma last week.

Me really got to go now,
UG! have to get hair right.
UG!'s friends are coming round soon –
We going clubbing tonight!

NEVER PUT CURRY UP YOUR NOSE

Never put curry up your nose,
You must fight your desire.
It's so flamin' hot when you blow your nose
You might just start a fire.

I'VE HAD MY CHIPS

I've just been to the chippy
And now I'm standing outside
Carrying two chips that are 8 feet tall
And just over 3 feet wide.

It's going to take me the rest of the week
To munch my way through these!
And all I said when I went in the shop
Was, "Hello, can I have large chips, please?"

TADPOLE

I caught a tadpole in a pond
And put him in a jar.
I wasn't sure what to feed him on
So I gave him a chocolate bar.

But that was a bad idea;
He ate and ate and ate
One chocolate bar after another –
Now my tadpole's a tad overweight.

So I bought him a fitness video
Which he watches to keep fit and train.
Now he's back to his old tadpole self;
You could say he feels spawn again!

THE BOY WHO LOVED BRUSSELS

There was once this boy who loved Brussels sprouts;
I'm telling you, that's all he ate!
You'd not find beans or sausage or chips,
Just Brussels on his plate.

If his mother made him sandwiches
What was between the bread?
Not cheese or spam, not eggs or ham,
Just juicy sprouts instead!

His parents took him to a posh restaurant,
A very fancy place.
But how embarrassed they both were
As he stuffed sprouts in his face!

Even Christmas dinner was different;
No giant turkey with veg on the side.
Just a little splash of gravy
On a Brussels sprout two feet wide!

Puddings and snacks were a little strange too;
The boy would sit watching the telly
Not devouring dessert of apple pie and cream
But a big bowl of sprout flavour jelly!

But this poem ends badly, I'm sorry to say,
For certain events came to pass.
For I'm sure that you know if you eat sprouts a lot
You'll build up a fair bit of gas.

The family was strolling back from the shops;
"My tummy hurts!" the young boy mumbled.
He dropped the shopping (which was mostly sprouts)
As his stomach gurgled and grumbled.

Then, with a huge **BANG!**, his bottom exploded.
A great **TTHHHRRRRPPPP!** shot out of his cheeks!
He flew into space, the last time they saw his face,
Though the smell hung round for weeks.

"Good grief!" said his mother as the green smoke cleared,
"Our boy has gone! What a mess!"
"But look on the bright side," his father chipped in,
"Our Brussels sprout bill will be less!"

So next time you're told, "Eat up your sprouts!"
Read this rhyme out loud.
If they still say, "Eat a few!" then they just want you to
Disappear in a smelly, green cloud!

ABB.

The world is such a crazy place,
Full of the strange and absurd.
Like why is abbreviation,
Such a very long word?

NEVER PUT GRANNY UP YOUR NOSE

Never put Granny up your nose,
Of that, there is no doubt!
Imagine when you picked it
And her teeth came flying out!

ELEPHANT JOHN

There was once an elephant called John,
The wrinkliest creature you've ever seen!
He'd had them for years round his eyes, round his ears,
Oh! To be smooth was his dream!

So he took a trip to the chemist
As he had a clever notion.
He grabbed off the shelf a present for himself:
A huge jar of anti-wrinkle lotion.

Now he sticks his trunk in the jar twice a day
And slaps it on, slippin' and sloppin',
Then rubs it in good, and I tell you he should!
It's taken ten years off him!

SHOE-LACE BOY

Shoe-lace Boy met String Girl,
He thought that she was hot!
They went out for a while, settled down
And thought they'd tie the knot.

QUINCY O'HARA
THE POLICE FORCE KOALA

It was Australia that tried it first
But it never quite caught on here.
Police dogs? YES! Police horse? Of course!
A police koala? Oh, dear!

It seemed like a great idea at first;
They had a little uniform made.
The word was put out on the streets
The cop koala must be obeyed.

They thought if someone had robbed a bank
And hidden up a tree,
Quincy Koala would climb up like a shot
And arrest him easily!

But things started going wrong
When they put him in a cop car;
His paws couldn't reach the pedals
So he didn't get very far.

Then, when **Quincy** tried to get tough,
Criminals thought he was jokin'.
They'd say, "Aah! How cute! Look at his little suit!"
And just want to cuddle and stroke him.

Quincy's career ended in shame.
His fellow officers said he'd go nuts
If he didn't have coffee and a regular supply
Of eucalyptus leaf doughnuts.

It looks like the police have a really tough job.
It looks like policeman look younger.
But at least policeman don't look like
Marsupials from **D**own-**U**nder.

NEVER PUT MONKEYS UP YOUR NOSE

Never put monkeys up your nose;
It's not that they will harm us
It's just that when you take a deep breath
You'll smell nothing but bananas.

ZOLA

Zola is a show squirrel
Who loves to sing and dance.
She can merengue and do the cha-cha
On each and every branch!

The woodland creatures love to watch
As she performs with style and guts.
The rabbits are all ears, the owls have a hoot
And the squirrels just go nuts!

ITCHY THE WITCH

The weirdest witch I ever met
Was Itchy the Witch, for sure!
She couldn't cast spells, her black cat smells,
And her evil potions were poor.

So she used her big, black cauldron
Not for brews, or curses of old,
But to boil batches of mushroom soup
For the homeless when it gets cold.

PUMPKIN

Once upon a time there was a pumpkin
Who was large and orange and round.
She was born in the pumpkin patch just up the road
And grew up from the ground.

She spent her days looking towards
Her very first Halloween.
It was a special time for pumpkins, she'd heard,
The best there'd ever been.

She concentrated on getting juicy and big
So she would look her best.
On October 1st she was sent to the shops,
Just like all the rest.

She sat in the shop, was picked up and squeezed,
Until somebody bought her.
A man took her home for a Halloween treat
For Florence, his small daughter.

Halloween came - pumpkin sat in the window
Of her new owners' old home.
She smiled a jagged pumpkin smile,
A vegetable all alone.

From the window she watched as the sun went down,
Her pumpkin heart excitedly beating.
What scenes she saw: people dressed up!
Young children trick or treating!

She started to wonder, as the moon came up,
What wonderful things were in store.
What would fill her head? What feelings inside
To treasure forever more?

But please don't expect a happy ending
For there's not one, it has to be said.
Her insides were scooped out to make pumpkin pie
And a candle was shoved in her head.

BREAD BOY

Bread Boy met Crumpet Girl;
Their relationship couldn't fail.
They got married one summer's day
Before the romance went stale.

But their perfect day was ruined
When they reached the reception room:
The guests all stood and said, "Three Cheers!"
Then toasted the bride and groom.

DOO DOO THE DODO

Doo Doo the Dodo
Is the last of her kind.
Why is that? I don't know
But she was quite a find.

The population of dodos
Is currently one.
The rest are extinct, killed off,
Quenched, all gone.

It seems that Doo Doo
Is the bird time forgot.
Why isn't she as dead
As a you know what?

The dodo called Doo Doo
Lives in my shed.
She's so sad, but you'd be too
If all your friends were dead.

I could've said, " Shoo, shoo!"
To that poor dodo
But it seems too cruel to do,
So she won't go go.

Doo Doo gets desperate
For dodo company.
But there are no more left
So she's had it, you see.

I've tried to find another
But I just can't, no way!
There's none at the zoo
And none on e-bay.

So conversation's a no-no
Which makes her "Boo Hoo!"
She's one lonely dodo,
Poor old Doo Doo.

I bought her a mirror
To help her recover.
Now my dodo is so-so
'Cos she thinks there's another!

Doo Doo now talks to
Her reflection all week
And it lifts me to see
A smile on her beak.

Now Doo Doo the Dodo
Is cheerful, not mopey!
But I can see why they died out,
They're so dodo dopey!

NEVER PUT LAWN-MOWERS UP YOUR NOSE

Never put lawn-mowers up your nose,
Not even for a dare.
You'll have to find some other way
To trim your nasal hair.

SUPER SPANIEL

Is it a bird? Is it a plane?
No, it's not, by heck!
It's next door's Cocker Spaniel
With a cape tied round his neck!

They call him Super Spaniel;
He isn't like the others.
As a pup he would beat up
His sisters and his brothers.

This mighty mutt has powers,
Leaps buildings in one bound;
Has x-ray eyes and radar ears
That pick up every sound!

But I wouldn't ever stroke him.
Listen, please, I beg.
You don't want to be in the firing line
When he cocks his super leg.

He got his puppy powers
From something that he ate –
A can of "Doggy Chunks" that was
Severely out of date.

But I'm afraid to report
(And this will drive you crazy!)
He doesn't use the powers he has;
This dog is doggone lazy.

Does he use his supersonic speed
To catch thieves and put them in jail?
Nope! Just to run in circles and
Try to catch his tail.

Super Spaniel has jaws of steel
But they don't get used at all.
The only action they ever see
Is chewing a squeaky ball.

And does he use his super sense of smell
To foil terrible crimes?
Nah! It's only used to try and sniff
Other dogs' behinds.

So let this dog's tale be a lesson to you,
And, if you have powers of your own,
Don't spend your time chasing cats
Or chewing on a bone.

Be anything but ordinary,
Not just another Joe Bloggs.
Be the best that you can be
And you won't go to the dogs.

OSTRICH MAN

One superhero you don't hear about
Is the amazing Ostrich Man.
I don't think he'll ever save the world
But he does the best that he can.

Unlike Superman he can't even fly!
He just tends to run around
And if ever sees any trouble coming
He'll stick his head underground!

THE HOLE IN THE SKY

Whilst walking along the other day
I noticed a hole in the sky.
I'm sure it wasn't there the day before,
So I began to wonder why.

I stared at the hole whilst trying to avoid
A woman collecting for the poor
But in doing so I nearly tripped over
A homeless man in a shop door.

I walked past some teenagers fighting
And a child driving his parent spare,
All of the time still pondering,
"Why is that big hole up there?"

Past a wall of graffiti I wandered,
Through a derelict housing estate.
I strolled as far as a burnt-out car
Where an old tramp sat on a crate.

I turned to the haggard man and asked,
"What is that big hole I see?"
He said with a sigh, "Son, that hole in the sky,
Is the place where God used to be."

THE 'TOILET' ROLL OF HONOUR

The King's England Press.
All my Family.   All my Friends.
Everybody I've met at the festivals, Theatres,
Schools, Libraries, Hospitals, Prisons, Islands,
Women's Institutes (!), Book Shops, Radio & TV
Stations whilst on my Poetry Performing Travels...

No need for names — You know who you are!

Thank You ALL.
CW